Painting a
with Li

A pictorial history of
Wheal Jane a Cornish tin mine.

by John Peck

PUBLISHED BY PECK PUBLICATIONS

ISBN 0-9552557-0-8

2006 © Text and photographs John Peck

PUBLISHED BY PECK PUBLICATIONS
Anzac Cottage
Chacewater
Truro
TR4 8LR
Website: www.johnpeckhandson.co.uk

Acknowledgments

I would not have been able to produce this book without help from the following people and would like to take this opportunity to thank them - Angela & Wayne Attwood, Bernard Ballard, Alan & Sheila Beattie, Tony Bennett, Peter Brett, Del Cod, Terry Cotton, Louise Hamilton, Madeleine & Terry Kay, Sylvia Owen, Robert Reading, Mike Shipp, and Alan Taylor.

Special thanks must go to Carol, my wife, without whose help and support this book would not have been finished. I would also like to thank Keith Poole for his help in the design, planning and production of this book.

Title page photograph:
John Brown and Barry Hopper drilling in a stope

Introduction

WHEAL JANE is situated three miles southwest of Truro in Cornwall. In the late sixties, a period of exploration in this mine was carried out by the owners, Goldfields. The ore reserves were proven and a new shaft was sunk, named Number 2, and an old shaft known as Clemow's was refurbished. From these shafts, levels were driven out at 100 foot (30 metres) intervals starting at 200 feet (60 metres) below the surface, known as 2 level and finishing at 15 level 1,540 feet (470 metres) underground. The Decline was an underground roadway initially running from 5 level to 11 level, at a gradient of 1 in 7. This gave access for the large machinery which was used in this mine. The main ore producing lode in the higher levels in Wheal Jane was B Lode whereas in the deeper levels it was known as Moor Shaft Lode, North and South branches. In 1971, with new shafts and the introduction of modern mining techniques, Wheal Jane became operational.

In 1972 the mine management advertised for a photographer. An interview process was held at which I was successful. Securing this post gave me a unique opportunity to combine my climbing and caving skills with my knowledge of photography. It was also the beginning of my long association with the mine. I found the work challenging and exciting. The working conditions were very wet, humid and usually very noisy. In this book I have combined many different aspects of mining as well as charting my development as a mining photographer. The night before a trip underground I would warm up the cameras and film. A typical visit would last for four hours, half a shift. Alongside cameras, film and flashguns I would carry an umbrella, in order to keep the camera dry and an orange for refreshment.

During this period I was privileged to become involved in many different projects and processes, both above and below ground. Choosing the photographs for this book has been a very difficult task. Where possible I have named the people in the photographs but, in the majority of them, I cannot identify them.

John Peck 2006

Contents

The Beginning

THIS section contains the early work I carried out in Wheal Jane and follows my development as a photographer in a new environment. This early work enabled the mine management to realise all the areas in which photography could be useful to them.

A Holmans 303 drill being used for stoping on B lode 2 level.

Stoping is the method used to extract the ore body from the rock. This is the first of a series of 12 photographs taken for an exhibition of industry in Cornwall.

Up until this point the mine had never had professional photographs taken underground. My remit was to produce a series of photographs for the exhibition.

The next four photographs are part of this series.

Brian Stapleton mucking out on 3 level B lode drive.

The function of the Eimco 21b machine is to throw the ore or waste over the machine and into the waiting wagon behind. It is operated by compressed air and runs on a track.

This series was taken using a twin lens reflex medium format camera (a Minolta autocord). Co-ordinating flashguns and miners was very difficult due to the noise levels and my inexperience.

Ore being deposited into an ore pass.

Taken on a sub-level between 2 and 3 levels we see ore being deposited into an ore pass. Ore passes are small raises, or vertical shafts, which interconnect levels underground. Raises can be used for ventilation, ladder ways (manway) and, as in this case, ore passing from one level to another.

The brief from the managers was that this series of photographs should actually show they were taken in a mine. I was anxious not to over light the subject particularly from the camera.

Placing lights where they were not being obstructed by props and cables was a challenge.

Surveying station.

Surveying is achieved by continually establishing new stations as work progresses. You can see here the number of this station on the roof above the surveyor's head. The line from the number is a plumb line down to the theodolite.

Battery powered locomotive pulling side tipper wagons.

Ore is being loaded at the lower end of a raise. There is a hydraulic swinging door at the bottom of the raise, which controls the flow of ore into the wagons.

A Dosco tunnelling machine with a moving cutting head.

This tunnelling machine, which is more often associated with coalmines, was being assessed for use at Wheal Jane. It was apparent at the time of taking the photograph that the machine was struggling due to the hardness of the rock.

By this time I felt my technique was improving. Using a small flash on the camera and a larger flash placed elsewhere, I was able to achieve more depth to the picture.

Building new headframe for Clemow's shaft.

A headframe is the means of supporting the sheave wheels of the hoisting ropes which pass down the shaft, which in turn raise or lower the cages or skips. At Clemow's shaft the headframe was generally used for hoisting ore and waste rock by means of skips.

   By this stage I was being asked to photograph site progress for the mine records.

New pump station on 10 level.

Usually someone accompanied me in the mine from the surveying department. On this occasion it was a shift boss, who did not appreciate the benefits of having a photographer in a mine (it only slowed the work down).

I wanted the wagon on the right to be moved for the picture so a helpful miner pushed the wagon under the bridge in the foreground with the help of a locomotive. Unfortunately, all the pipes that passed under it became disconnected. The result of this was a lot of swearing and cursing from miners in other locations as they lost all their compressed air. I still managed to persuade someone to pose for me.

Scoop tram in the decline.

Used for carrying loads of ore and waste rock in the decline, the front bucket of this machine could carry 2.5 tons and was operated by a diesel engine with catalytic converters fitted. This made the machine so efficient that it removed all carbon monoxide from the exhaust. It was known as an articulated load, haul dump machine (LHD). The "decline" is an inclined underground roadway allowing vehicular access between different levels.

To take this photograph I placed the camera on a tripod, opened the shutter on the camera and in total darkness I walked in front of the camera into a tunnel and then fired the flash before returning to the camera and closing the shutter. The Scoop tram operator was not allowed to move during the operation. On this occasion I used Ektachrome slide film 400 ASA 35mm.

Jarvis Clark dump truck.

This machine could carry 12 tons in the decline. The bucket attached to this machine had to be cut in half to enable it to be lowered down the shaft and was then welded together again underground.

The same photographic technique was used as in the previous photograph.

Welding in garage 9 level.

All servicing of large machinery took place at this underground garage. It was situated on the decline, which ran from 5 level down to 11 level, later extended to 15 level. The Wheal Jane levels were one hundred feet apart, starting at 200 feet (60 metres) below the surface. The fitter in the photograph is repairing a Scoop tram.

Accident site on 5 level.

A lot of the ground at Wheal Jane was structurally not very sound. Steel supports (sets) were being erected to support the roof when this accident occurred. In this photograph the roof had collapsed. Whilst I was taking the photographs small rocks were still falling.

By this stage the mine management was realising the benefits of having a professional photographer available to take photographs underground. On this occasion I was asked to photograph a site following a serious accident. Previous to this, the mine management, unions and inspectors would have relied on surveyors' drawings and measurements following a serious accident. The photographs proved to be a very useful accompaniment to the surveyor's report and from this point on I was on call for whenever a serious accident occured.

Alan Taylor inspecting the wooden sets 3 level.

Wood was still used to shore up loose ground in some places in Wheal Jane

Stoping

STOPING is the main production method in a tin mine. Once a lode is identified, its tin content assessed and the necessary development work completed, stoping would begin.

Overhand stoping is when the miner is drilling upwards into the lode to enable the ore to be blasted out, forming a void known as a stope.

Overhand stoping 9 level.

Long hole stoping.

Using this method of stoping the miner will drill numerous long holes upwards, across the width of the lode. The holes can be 50 feet (17 metres) long. The ore will then be blasted out into the available space creating a new stope. The Scoop tram or Cavo loader will then load the ore.

To take this photograph it was necessary for me to stand in the stope. The roof could be as much as 200 feet (60 metres) above my head.

Long hole stoping.

This view shows the face that will be blasted out to create a stope.

Sand fill stope.

Approximately 1% of the ore extracted from the mine contained tin. This posed a problem of waste disposal for the above ground processing plant. The waste, consisting mainly of fine quartz and mica, was transported underground as slurry in pipes to fill stopes and provide ground support when settled.

Here, open stopes are being experimentally filled with waste sand. The men are constructing wooden drains to take away the water that is used to carry the sand in flexible pipes underground. The experiment failed due to excessive wear in the pipes from the sand and water.

Group of miners having croust.

Left to right -
Barry Hooper, Cookie, John Brown, and Dinga Bell. The men are having their croust sitting on the wooden drains in the sand fill stope.

Overhand stoping

Whilst photographing the sand fill stope, I saw two men drilling while a tractor light briefly passed behind them. They were standing on the back filled sand and drilling upwards (overhand stoping).

This was a picture I could not resist trying to recreate. I had three exposures left on the film. I set a flash light behind the men with a highly sensitive photo electronic switch attached, which had been designed by my son. There was also a small flash on the camera.

The men would not stop work, which meant there was a lot of moisture and dirt in the air. In the first two attempts the large flash did not fire. Before the third attempt I ran under the drill and reconnected the switch and this time it fired.

A poster of the photograph was made entitled Cornish Tin for Britain.

Processing the Ore

THE first crushing of the ore takes place underground. Once it is brought to the surface, it is crushed further and ground into fine sand in order to release tin and other important metals.

The secondary (fine) ore pile

This is the ore after it has passed through two crushers. The nearest headframe in the picture is that of Clemow's shaft used to hoist the ore to the surface. The shaft on the left, known as Number 2 shaft, was used to hoist men and machinery.

Ore conveyor on the surface.

This conveyor is transporting ore to the ball mill. An x-ray process was used to help grade the ore prior to processing. Although Wheal Jane was opened primarily as a tin mine, many other valuable minerals were also present in the ore. The x-ray process monitored the percentage of valuable minerals within the ore. This process was known as head grading.

This is one of the few photographs I took using only the available light.

Adrian Perry operating the ball mill.

Prior to processing, the ore was ground by the ball mill whose continually rotating steel balls ground the ore into sand. This enabled the separation of the valuable minerals from the rock.

Flotation was one of the processes whereby certain valuable minerals were removed from the ore. To achieve this ore was floated and the minerals attached themselves to bubbles thereby allowing extraction.

Left. *Flotation floor, Wheal Jane mill.*

Shaking table.

The table vibrates, separating the different metals by weight. There were a total of 68 tables in the Wheal Jane mill during its most productive phase. The shaking table was based on old mining techniques when water and the ore bearing material were gently shaken on a vanning shovel.

Left. *Flotation cells in the mill.*
Here you can see the individual flotation cells. Other minerals, besides tin, extracted by this process, were sulphides of copper and zinc, leaving arsenic and iron as waste material.

Raise boring

THERE were two machines which were synonymous with Wheal Jane, thereby making it different from any other mine in the county. These are the diesel powered Scoop tram and the raise borer. The raise borer was an electro-hydraulic boring machine which could bore a hole 6 feet (1.82 metres) in diameter, to a depth of 200 feet (60 metres), safely and quickly. The machine was introduced into Wheal Jane in 1977. Before this machine a raise required men having to climb up into the area of the shaft which had just been blasted, to drill and place more explosives. Each time they did this there was a risk of a rock fall. They could be doing this for several months in order to drill a raise between levels. The raise borer meant a raise could now be excavated safely in weeks instead of months.

Raise borer on 7 level.

In this photograph you can see the machine being operated by Richard Sterratt. This photograph was taken by available light, unusual underground. This was because electricity had to be brought to the site and flood lighting used due to the intricate nature of the operation.

Setting the foundations for the machine.

Surveyor Dave Clark left and linesman Pete Robinson at work.

Pilot bit breaking through into 9 level.

Here we can see Roy Horsington examining the bit for damage after it had broken through on 9 level, 60 metres below the raise boring machine on 7 level. The pilot bit is then attached to the drill string.

A drill string consists of one metre length rods which, when consecutively added to the drill bit, allows the pilot bit to work further away from the base of the machine.

Reamer being attached to the drill string on 9 level.

Below.
Reamer attached to drill string.

After breakthrough has been achieved the reamer is attached to the bottom of the drill string. Hardened steel discs and tungsten tipped side rollers are attached to it.

This enables the reamer to cut the rock to the required dimensions.
In this photograph the reamer has been lowered to show the first cut.
The cross you can see in the photograph is where the surveyor estimated breakthrough would occur. This has been missed by less than one metre, remarkable after starting the work 200 feet (60 metres) away.

The reamer on 9 level.

In this photograph the reamer is actually turning slowly and is in the process of being drawn back to 7 level and towards the raise borer. Note the tungsten side rollers which hopefully will leave the raise with smooth sides.

This series of photographs was taken using a Bronica medium format single lens reflex camera and HP5 120 film. The photographs were always taken when the operation took place, which was often at night or other unsociable times.

Ore pass 1300 level to 1500 level.

This photograph was taken to show long hole grouting in a raise bored raise. The pipes you can see are ready to have liquid cement pumped into them. This process was needed to try and stop water ingress.

In order to take this photograph we climbed up 200 feet (60 metres) using ladders. It was both very wet and hot. It felt like climbing a 200-foot Jacuzzi. Note the smooth walls, which make them ideal for easy passage of ore or for ventilation. Also note my boots at the top of the ladder.

Miners posing.

Here we can see miners and technicians posing with the raise boring machine in the background.

From left to right we have Michael Harrison, Mike Bacon and Richard Sterratt.

Raise bore bearing.

This photograph taken for insurance purposes, shows a fault in the bearing. It was taken in the engineering workshop using the available natural light. I was able to use my newly acquired Bronica with Nikkor lens.

John Mortimor with the pilot bit of the raise borer.

This was the only time I was on site as an accident happened. Just after this was taken a rock fell from the roof above.
The following two photographs show the scene after the rock fall.

Fallen rock.

The white cross
marks the rock which
fell from the roof.

**_Group awaiting the
rescue team._**

As a result of the rock fall the
miner in the middle had a
broken ankle.
The team are waiting for
rescue to transport the injured
man out of the mine.

1978 The Mine is Threatened

Union meeting at Wheal Jane.

GOLDFIELDS, as the current owners of Wheal Jane planned to close the mine. The adjacent mine, Mount Wellington, that was owned by another company, had switched off its water pumps on closure, affecting the water levels in Wheal Jane. This meant extra pumping costs to prevent flooding. A union meeting was held in April 1978 at which a decision was made to hold a protest march in London in an attempt to keep the mine open.

Hyde Park Corner.

The protest march gathered at Hyde Park Corner. There was heavy media interest in this event.

Miners and their supporters marching through the streets of London.

Their intention was to persuade the government to put Wheal Jane and Mount Wellington mines on care and maintenance while new financial arrangements could be made.

Number 10 Downing Street.

Alan Taylor, Cliff Elson and Daphne Brown are part of the group presenting a petition to 10 Downing St. Following this, Goldfields closed the mine but the Government paid to keep the mine clear of water until another company could possibly be found to take over ownership.

Mike Shipp and Jim Trew in B Lode, "East" Wheal Jane (early 20th century workings).

In the period following closure the government of the day paid to keep the mine pumps working. Mike Shipp, chief Surveyor, and Jim Trew, Mine Manager, remained at the mine for care and maintenance purposes.

In this photograph we are in a disused area of the mine known as East Wheal Jane. A visit was required to this site to check on the water levels. I was invited along, at my own risk, to record the site. I was struck by the silence around me; usually visits to the mine are filled with a lot of noise, heat and dust.

Right.
Mike Shipp and Jim Trew are examining an old water wheel found in disused workings deep in the mine. This wheel was probably used to drive ventilation bellows to give miners air when working.

Note the Davy lamp in the photograph. This was a vital piece of safety equipment when exploring old workings. If the flame went out we knew we had to leave the area.

Mike Shipp examining an old wagon.

This photograph is taken from a similar position as the previous picture

An old water wheel.

Water in the main drive 9 level.

In 1979 the mine was under new ownership (RTZ) who also purchased Mount Wellington. I was asked to take photographs to show the state of disrepair before refurbishment began. Water is normally channelled away from drives.

Note the stalactites of ochre in the roof and walls, which were a rare sight in Wheal Jane.

Mud in the drive.

This build up of mud occurred in an 18 month period when mining was on hold.

Renovations on the surface.

Work now proceeded at a pace to repair and refurbish all equipment, both underground and on the surface.

Here we can see the pylon to the conveyor belt in a state of disrepair. Note the corroded legs where refurbishment has already started.

The County Adit

The twin tunnels of the County Adit.

THE County Adit is a very old system of tunnels which is used to drain the mines in the Gwennap and Chacewater areas of Cornwall which includes Wheal Jane and Mount Wellington. The system consists of approximately 39 miles of tunnels and in the past was run as a separate company. The sole purpose was to drain the mines. Individual mines paid a fee to be part of the system. Two parallel tunnels were driven from just below Twelveheads to Hale Mills where the systems separated, one branching towards United Downs and the St. Day area and the other continuing under the Poldice Valley towards Wheal Busy. During the 19th century at least forty mines were part of this system.

The management at Wheal Jane decided to improve the efficiency of the adit in order to save themselves pumping costs.

Here we have a photograph of the twin tunnels, which extended through Twelveheads as far as Hale Mills. At this point, due to the shallow depth and the loose ground it passes through, it is both collapsed and blocked in several places. It was because of these factors a new tunnel and portal were constructed enabling this shallow ground to be bypassed.

Portal to the new County Adit.

This photograph shows the ground being prepared for the new portal. On the right of the photograph lies the existing entrance to the County Adit.

Reggie Tellam at the finished portal of the County Adit.

Water from the Wellington pumps.

Here we can see water being channelled towards the Carnon River from the Mount Wellington pumps via the Wellington Adit.

Water in the County Adit.

While tunnels were being explored for blockages, the miners and I would often be up to our waist in water. In order to take photographs I needed to waterproof my cameras. Whilst in the adit, keeping the equipment clean was difficult; the ochre clung to everything and anything. In the foreground is Alex Grant, Mining Engineer, and in the distance is Mike Shipp, Mine Surveyor.

Inside the County Adit.

These are very old sections of the County Adit, along which there are many collapses, which have caused blockages. The only way to clear the debris is to use the old method of one man and a wheelbarrow. The debris is then taken to the various shafts and is removed by using a crane and a kibble, a large bucket with chains attached.

Removal of debris.

Here we can see one of the County Adit shafts in Wheal Maid valley. The crane and kibble are being used to remove debris from this shaft.

New launder in a stope.

This new launder has been installed to take water through a stope to the County Adit. This is to prevent water going deeper into the mine and hence saving on pumping costs. The reason for taking this photograph was to show the completed work. Mike Shipp can be seen in the distance.

I was often asked what I photographed underground. This section contains a small number of photographs of the general machinery and exploratory work not covered in the specific projects that I photographed.

Terry Cotton and Derek James in Cardoza shaft United Mines.

These old workings were accessed from Francis shaft via a mobile headframe, to give access for diamond drilling, testing for possible tin reserves. This photograph shows the remains of a pumping rod from a beam engine at 700 feet (210 metres) below surface. I was told that this would be a dry area. Never trust a miner! Their interpretation of dry is different from mine. It was very, very muddy. I have never been able to fully remove the ochre that attached itself to my camera.

The camera I was using at this stage was a Mamiya 6.45 with 75mm lens.

Graham Jasper by the ventilation fans.

These fans were used to force ventilation into Wheal Jane from the Mount Wellington shaft. Their size was 60 inches (1.5 metres) and they were located on 3 level Wheal Jane and 2 level Mount Wellington, the point where the two mines joined underground.

To take this photograph I descended at Mount Wellington and walked through to Wheal Jane, a distance of approximately two miles.

A Cavo 310 loader on sub level 9 off the decline. This is a compressed air operated mucking machine. Note the rubber tyres, which means it is not limited by needing to be on tracks. It can also be operated by remote control in areas which are deemed unsafe. This machine has its own tipper attached at the rear making it easier to dump the ore into a raise.

Here you see it operated by Dave Honey. Also note the bright yellow colour; this denotes a very new machine.

Eimco 24 loader.

A conventional loader which operates on tracks. It is evident from this photograph that this is not a new machine.

Granby wagons being loaded from a raise.

The machinery is so large that the challenge was to be able to get some depth into the photograph.

Tramming on 7 level.

Here we see a locomotive drawing 5 ton Granby wagons.

The lighting of this photograph was achieved by using an open shutter and three flashguns operated by strategically placed miners. The instructions to the miners were to fire their flashes when they saw my flash go off; when I saw their flashes I closed the shutter.

Granby wagons tipping into an ore pass.

The Granby 5 ton wagons are unloading the ore through steel parallel bars known as a grizzly. The bars are placed 6 inches (15cms) apart. This stops the larger rocks falling into the raise and down to the crusher. The miners will reduce the larger rocks to enable them to pass through the grizzly.

This was a very noisy environment in which to take a photograph. Hand signals were often used to communicate.

Tamrock/Jumbo in the decline.

This machine was used for drilling new tunnels particularly on the decline. It was moved by diesel power and the drills were operated by electric hydraulics.

Left.
New tyres for a Tamrock.

Taken on 9 level garage. This was the first visit underground for these tyre fitters. When they arrived to do this job they had not realised they would be working in a garage 900 feet (270 metres) underground

Watertight doors 9 level.

These doors separated the shaft from the garage. The purpose was to protect the shaft from flooding. It was disconcerting to walk through watertight doorways. I always hoped I was on the right side of them in the event of a flood. See plan.

A Clayton locomotive.

Les Oliver drives the new Clayton locomotive at Wheal Jane. The photograph was taken outside number two shaft, with Clemow's shaft in the background.

Shaft Sinking

EARLY in 1981 I was called into the office and told they would be extending Clemow's shaft to 1500 level. It was thought that the whole operation would last about 18 months and I would be required to photograph progress every two or three weeks. This is a process which has rarely been photographed before due to the difficult conditions. Most photographs would have to be taken around the men whilst they worked and not posed.

This was one of the most exciting projects I photographed in Wheal Jane. This section contains a few of those photographs.

A temporary sinking winder being erected on 10 level Clemow's shaft.

A new winder was needed providing the means to carry men and materials up and down the shaft. This was part of the preparations needed for deepening Clemow's shaft. It was being extended from 11 level to 15 level where a new crusher would be installed.

Shaft sinking tool kit.

During shaft sinking, each working shift would have a specific task.

In this photograph we can see the team in charge of preparing the way. They would drill and place explosives before blasting could occur. The tool kit containing drills, drill heads and compressed air delivery can be seen arriving at the workplace.

Forming the shaft walls.

In order to stabilize the shaft walls and prevent water ingress the shaft is lined with cement which is piped down the shaft.

In this photograph the new shaft walls can be seen above the men and, below them the scaffolding can be seen holding the wooden shuttering in place. The shuttering is used to hold the cement in place whilst it sets within the shaft.

Long hole grouting at 14 level.

In order to keep the shaft as dry as possible, a series of long holes are drilled in the sides of the shaft. Then cement is pumped under pressure into these holes to fill in all the cracks and fissures. This is a continual process as the shaft is sunk. The concrete structure above the men is the new shaft walls. The white splashes, which are evident in the photograph, is water falling; it was like being out in the rain. It was not possible to talk or issue verbal instructions in this environment due to the noise. Hand signals had to be agreed before arriving on the site.

Kibble arriving at 13 level.

The kibble is attached to the winder and in this photograph you can see men arriving at 13 level, the current sump (bottom) of the shaft. Colin Jones, project manager, can be seen facing the camera.

The large pipe at the top of the photograph provides

ventilation. The kibble was the only method of travelling in the shaft and was a new experience for me. The Kibble could only carry three people at a time. This was quite a tight squeeze with my photographic equipment, which consisted of a rucksack with large waterproofed flashguns, and a metal camera case. I'd never travelled in a bucket before but it didn't sway as much as I expected.

Because this was a very busy area, once I was on site I had to remain there until there was a break in the shift.

Cactus grab operating at 13 level.

The cactus grab is being used to load the kibble with broken rock. This operation required good communications, as the operator could not see the men or where the grab was landing. A signal system was used to co-ordinate the process. In order to load the rock the cactus grab had to be lowered to the floor, pick up the rock, be raised and swung pendulum like across the kibble.

This photograph shows the rock being released, by the man on the left, into the kibble. If you look at the bottom right hand corner of the shaft, you can just see the submersible pump which keeps the water at a bearable level for the workers in the sump.

Preparing for blasting in Clemow's at 1500 feet.

In this photograph the miner is ramming home the dynamite into the predrilled holes in the rock. The box of detonators can be seen above the miner and to the left.

The technique I used to take photographs in the shaft was to use a 35mm SLR camera with a small flash attached in a waterproof bag. The film I used was Ilford XP2. A willing miner held a second large flash with a highly sensitive photo electronic switch attached, which was also in a waterproof bag! He would stand and direct the flash according to my hand signals. One problem was that if the beam of a miner's hat lamp went across the electronic switch, the lamp would fire. This meant that several seconds would have to pass before I could take a photograph. Other problems were that the flash batteries had a limited life and I could not change films in this environment. I therefore had to be very economic with the photographs I took.

Construction of a crusher in the shaft at 1500 feet.

Massive girders are being placed in a large cavern at the bottom of the extended shaft. This will form a platform for the crusher. Crushers are always placed at the bottom of a shaft (see plan). This is because ore can be passed down the various raises by means of gravity. After the initial crushing the ore is then raised to the surface. It was a relief to be in a much bigger space to take this photograph; however, as you can see, the water is still falling around us.

The End is in Sight

EARLY in 1986 the tin price started to fall which threatened the survival of Cornish mining. As a result of this politicians and the media began to take an interest in Cornish mining. Wheal Jane started to receive visits from interested politicians. Now I was having an opportunity to be a press photographer as the press was not generally invited underground.

The book concludes with two aerial photographs of the mine site.

David Penhaligan on a march.

With the slump in the price of tin a request was made to the government to help keep the mines operational. A protest march was organised in London. Here you can see David Penhaligan, local M.P., talking to a reporter.

Dr. David Owen M.P. visits.

After the appeal to the government for money, various politicians visited the mine. Here we see David Owen talking to Brian Calver, the Managing Director of Wheal Jane.

Roy Hattersley M.P. visits.

Bill Hobba, underground manager, can be seen making a point to Roy Hattersley.

A visit of the Zimbabwean minister for mines.

The minister and Bill Hobba examine a Scoop tram and an almost naked miner on the decline. It was fairly normal for miners to be scantily clad due to the very high humidity and heat.

David Harris M.P. visits.

David Harris can be seen here talking to a group of miners having their croust on 7 level station.

An aerial photograph of Wheal Jane.

This was a very memorable trip for me. A series of aerial photographs were required of Wheal Jane, Carnon Valley, Delabole Slate and Mount Wellington. I have included the appropriate ones in this book. The first shows Wheal Jane site with the mill in the foreground. The second shows Mount Wellington with the Twelveheads Bissoe road in the foreground, and the old mineral tramway crossing in the foreground. The entrance to the County Adit can also be seen in the dark area bottom left. Equipment used was one helicopter with door removed, Mamiya 6.45 with 75mm lens and XP2 roll film. We flew between 500 and 1,000 feet (270-340 metres) for photographic purposes. For this trip I had to wear a throat mike to enable me to communicate with the pilot and to instruct him on the position to be in for the photographs. It was very cold; I would sit on my hands to keep them warm between shots.

Aerial shot Mount Wellington.

Wheal Jane finally closed in 1991 - 3.9 million tonnes of ore had been processed at the mill. The gross tonnage of metals produced was tin 23,800, zinc 96.000 and copper 9,610 the mine also produced small amounts of wolfrom and silver.

Glossary

Adit	A tunnel which drains water from the mine.
Croust	A meal or tea break.
Crusher	Used to reduce the rock.
Decline	A sloping underground roadway.
Diamond drilling	A technique by which a core of rock is removed for sampling.
Drive	A level tunnel.
Grizzly	Steel parallel bars which stop larger rocks passing through.
Headframe	A mechanism which supports the sheave wheels of the hoisting ropes allowing access to the mine.
Kibble	A large bucket with chains attached.
Launder	A wooden structure for passing water over a space.
Level	A tunnel 30 metres apart vertically (in Wheal Jane).
Lode	Where the ore is present in the rock.
Long hole grouting	A method of filling in cracks in the rock face.
Manway	A walkway or ladder way.
Mucker	A machine for digging out broken rock.
Ore	Raw material economically capable of being worked for valuable metals.
Portal	Entrance to a tunnel or adit.
Raise	Small shafts which interconnect levels underground.
Raise borer	A machine used to bore a raise.
Reamer	A tool used to enlarge an existing hole.
Scoop tram	A large diesel driven load haul and dumper.
Sub level	A tunnel 15 metres vertically above or below and between the main levels.
Sump	The lowest point at which the water will gather.
Stope	The space left when the ore bearing rock has been removed (sometimes known as a gunniss).
Tamrock	A drilling machine for creating level tunnels.
Theodolite	A surveying instrument used for precisely measuring longitudinal and vertical angles.
Tramming	The movement of wagons underground.
Wheal	Mine
Winder	A mechanism by which men, machinery and ore are hauled up and down a shaft.